THE
CURLY
PYJAMA
LETTERS

To Mary Ellen
Merry Christmas

Michael Leunig

Also by Michael Leunig

THE
CURLY
PYJAMA
LETTERS

MICHAEL LEUNIG

VIKING

Viking
Penguin Books Australia Ltd
487 Maroondah Highway, PO Box 257
Ringwood, Victoria 3134, Australia
Penguin Books Ltd
Harmondsworth, Middlesex, England
Penguin Putnam Inc.
375 Hudson Street, New York, New York 10014, USA
Penguin Books Canada Limited
10 Alcorn Avenue, Toronto, Ontario, Canada M4V 3B2
Penguin Books (NZ) Ltd
Cnr Rosedale and Airborne Roads, Albany, Auckland, New Zealand
Penguin Books (South Africa) (Pty) Ltd
24 Sturdee Avenue, Rosebank, Johannesburg 2196, South Africa
Penguin Books India (P) Ltd
11, Community Centre, Panchsheel Park, New Delhi 110 017, India

First published by Penguin Books Australia 2001

1 3 5 7 9 10 8 6 4 2

Illustrated by Michael Leunig
Designed by George Dale, Penguin Design Studio
Typeset in Palatino light
Scanning and separations by Splitting Image P/L, Blackburn, Victoria
Produced in Australia by Australian Book Connection

National Library of Australia
Cataloguing-in-Publication data:

Leunig, Michael 1945– .

The curly pyjama letters.
ISBN 0 670 04023 1.

1. Caricatures and cartoons – Australia. 2. Australian wit and humour, pictorial. I. Title.

741.5994

www.penguin.com.au

to unusual friendships

The town of Curly Flat

Introduction

THE TWENTY-NINE LETTERS here published amount to a small fragment of the vast correspondence which is known to have taken place between lone voyager Vasco Pyjama and his friend and mentor Mr Curly of Curly Flat. How this handful of letters has come to light is something of a mystery, except to say that they simply 'appeared' as a small bundle tied up with a thin blue ribbon – the sort that can be found on a baby's bootie or bonnet.

Curiously they are not dated, and in the absence of an apparent chronology or thematic sequence (with the exception of some obvious pairings) they are presented in this volume in a 'whimsical/poetic' order sympathetic, it is hoped, to the spontaneous, meandering nature of the relationship which is evident between the correspondents.

Apart from what can be gleaned from the writing, precious little is known about the curriculum vitae of either Vasco Pyjama or Mr Curly. Rumours of sightings and snippets of heresay have come and gone over the years regarding past and present circumstances, but they all elude substantiation. Contradictory tales emerge and the image of the Curly–Pyjama world fades into the mist; the signal disappears and the mystery deepens. The truth could be that souls like Vasco and Curly are with us always, eternally present and reliably under our noses, it's just that we are unable to see them; we are blind to their realness, their openness, their sheer improbability and their noble innocence. Perhaps they become invisible when our gaze becomes too fierce, and then we declare that they are mystical, enigmatic and elusive. Yet they stand humbly and simply before us – at our feet while we search the clouds for their existence.

It is generally accepted, however, that Mr Curly still lives somewhere by the shores of Lake Lacuna near Curly Flat where, amongst other pursuits, he is actively and passionately absorbed in matters of horticulture, birdwatching, music and winemaking. His wines from the Curly Flat vineyard are legendary for the gentleness, cheerfulness and lyricism of their intoxication. Domestic contentment and ease with the natural world appear to be Mr Curly's major attributes or achievements – but not at the expense of an expressive and spirited personal style.

Vasco Pyjama probably started his life in Curly Flat, where the great friendship began, but his searching and restless nature has compelled him into his great voyage of discovery – the circumnavigation of his own world. In the company of his direction-finding duck (a sort of living compass which, according to Vasco, 'always points toward new joys'), he has left his home and wandered far and wide into his uncharted world,

Vasco Pyjama's perilous voyage through the dreaded
Strait of a Thousand Lighthouses

risking, finding, enjoying and observing much. He is clearly the more troubled and vulnerable of the two; more easily shaken and bruised; more prone to self-doubt, disillusionment or spiritual intoxication – and perhaps possessed of a lonelier, more ecstatic vision.

Despite their different natures, the two friends have created a common language style – a shared personal dialect which might be variously described as Naïve Formal, Mock Victorian, Reserved Romantic or Quaint

Melodramatic. Were it a spoken language it would sound affected, perhaps, but in the written form it is clearly a language of unique personal protocol, as is often found in conversations between creative and intelligent minds in awe of life's complex grandeur, beauty and pathos. In the language of protocol much can be said and read between the lines, between the words; it serves well the discussion of philosophy which is both finely sensed and deeply felt, as is the

In Curly Flat unforeseen circumstances are celebrated ...
accidents bring out the best in people

case in the Curly–Pyjama correspondence. True formality allows for and provides great creative space and great lyrical acoustics.

Letters, of course, imply distance – often huge distance in space and time – and between separated dear friends there is often, in their mutual correspondence, an underlying yearning for each other's actual presence, an emotional undertone which flows from a thwarted passionate impulse to simply *be* with and hold the other in all their sensuality and truth. Such passion sometimes requires a certain linguistic bearing to make the heartache more bearable.

It is obvious to anyone but an emotional philistine that Curly and Vasco love each other and that, though they both enjoy their separate and differing lives, they also long for the day when they can be together again in peace and merriment on the sunny slopes overlooking the shores of Lake Lacuna. And of course the duck would be included. Perhaps they are there now, the three of them – reunited at Curly Flat. Nobody knows. Perhaps new facts will come to light, but for the moment all we have are these letters and the thin blue ribbon which held them together.

Michael Leunig

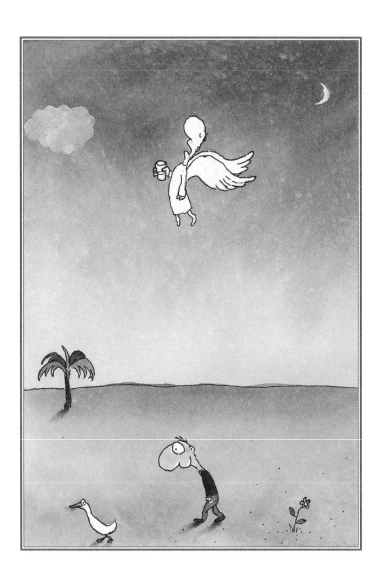

Dear Mr. Curly,

I have not written to you for quite some time, I suppose because there has been very little to report. My journey appears to have developed into a process of steady plodding which I rather like. When you plod, everything seems to take forever and forever is a lovely thing once you stop being scared of it.

Strange, how something that takes a lot of time can give a feeling that there _is_ a lot of time — and a lot of space and a good measure of ease. So onward I plod, through beautiful things and terrible things, too numerous to mention, with my duck

ahead of me and my gargling angel to
protect me from above. I am well and I
hope you are too.

Best wishes; yours truly,

Vasco Pyjama.

P.S. Is it "gargling" angel or "guardian" angel?
Somebody once suggested it should be
"guardian" but I grew up believing it was
"gargling"—"My gargling angel" and that's
how I think of it. Oh well, whatever; it
seems to care for me!

Dear Mr. Curly,

blessings and warm salutations —— long time no sea! Just a brief note to tell you I am presently staying in a very strange and wobbly place and in spite of a shaky start, I am beginning to enjoy myself. All varieties of wobbling seem to abound here as a natural condition of life. Wobbling, wiggling, waggling, wavering, fluttering, fluctuating shimmering: all actions, all thoughts, all feelings and all of matter itself seem animated by these qualities. Nothing is firm, nothing is solid; and because there is no expectation of firmness here, there seems to be no problem with all this fluidity, in fact there appear to be many pleasing and delightful outcomes. Surprisingly, life seems to proceed successfully enough and I am learning much about living with movement and the ever changing shape of large and small things. I still find it a bit difficult to write when the ground under my feet starts moving as it is doing right now. Perhaps the best way to deal with this particular situation is to bid you a fond adieu — after all, there comes a time to put down one's pen and to rest one's tongue. Adieu, adieu — with love, Vasco Pyjama.

P.S. THE DUCK IS WELL.

12

Dear Vasco,
Summer is almost with us here in Curly
Flat and the season of the asparagus
is all but finished. Never have I enjoyed
such delicious asparagus curls as the ones
we harvested this spring. How remarkable
and odd that this delectable shoot, this
point of emergence into the rough, wild
world is so tender and full of goodness,
and how exploited and wounded it is
for these beautiful qualities.

How interesting Vasco, that growth
meets so much resistance, attracts
such brutality, its creations are so
constantly plundered — and yet it

persists and is tender — troubled
and tender! Growth is troubled
and tender. C'est la vie.

One more thing: asparagus certainly
is food for thought!

Protect yourself Vasco,
yours truly

Mr. Curly.
xxx

Dear Mr. Curly,

I am writing to tell you that I expect to be in Curly Flat for Christmas and look forward to seeing you. The duck is waddling wearily (but steadfastly) in a homeward direction and has got that faraway, forbearing look in its eye. Naturally I am following and if most things go well we should be moving along the shores of Lake Lacuna by Christmas eve on the final stretch of our journey back to some peace and quiet.

The world through which we have been travelling seems to be in the grip of a particular madness. I can think of no other word for it but "mania", yet many other words are used; such are the many and varied faces of mania. It is called "passion". It is called "excitement." It is even called "celebration." And now whenever I hear words such as energy, entertainment, information, growth, achievement, great, fast, brilliant, talent, vision or more, I am aware of the probability that mania is on the loose and is being rewarded and cultivated, and that the possibility of peacefulness, wisdom and a good life is being further spoiled and neglected. Oh dear, enough of this.

It will be lovely to be back in Curly Flat again and to be with you on that beautiful, special, dark night.

best pre-christmas wishes
yours sincerely,
Vasco Pyjama

P.S. COULD YOU PLEASE ORDER, FROM THE BAKERY, A LARGE CHRISTMAS CAKE FOR THE DUCK.

P.P.S. COULD YOU MAKE THAT <u>EXTRA LARGE</u>, JUST TO BE ON THE SAFE SIDE. THANKS.

17

Dear Vasco

I'm sorry to hear that you are presently finding the world to be such an unhappy place. Actually, about two thirds of humanity _are_ fairly miserable and will remain so. The problem is that the one third who are contented enough are pretty well invisible. It seems to me that happy souls are inclined to hide or disguise their contentment as a way of protecting and preserving it; so you don't get to see much obvious happiness and you might easily imagine that all the world is depressed. But human happiness exists! It is truly the love that dares not speak its own name. Nothing attracts so much hate and envious attack as simple human happiness. What an appalling fact of life. There is a great cruel ongoing war waged compulsively by the miserable majority against the contented. No wonder happiness lies low! And you will never read about this war in the newspapers — not directly — because it has been going on since time began and it is regarded as the normal and proper state of affairs. Although happiness is greatly outnumbered it has wisdom on its side — and a great keen love of life — and an instinct for survival — and a vision which enables it to see far ahead and behind and through the darkest night — and an unfailing ability to recognise its own kind as well as the enemy which would destroy it. So it survives. Against all odds it survives — but almost invisibly — <u>the invisible third!</u> They move about at dawn and in the evening; on the backroads and byways; they often look almost drab and you might easily not notice them unless you are one of them; they lie hidden in the landscape; they lie in the long grass watching the clouds; they laze in secluded dells hearing the music of small birds; they rarely make the news. But you can find them Vasco, and they can find you; there are ways. But take good care — this is a very nasty war, this war against happiness — a primitive, brutal war. Be brave Vasco —

yours truly

Mr. Curly

x x x

Dear Vasco,

I have just remembered something!

Each day is a lifetime.

In the morning we are born.

The day lies before us: vast and bright and new. We say, "Good Morning!" as a prayer and blessing because a good morning may bring a good day and a good life.

By lunchtime we have come to mid-life.
We take a hearty meal and rest. We are
in the midst of the day's demands and we
are doing our plain duty in attending to
them. This is how we find out the truth about
ourselves and the truth about the world.
What a thing to find out! But we have to.

The evening is calm. We sup and reflect. We ready ourselves for the end and prepare for the hereafter: for the next day: a bit of tidying; a little reparation, some shared peace and pleasure and then a prayer on the pillow. An owl hoots. "It was a good life" we say. A cricket sings, the lamp fades and it is over. We die.

So good evening Vasco;
good day to you and
good morning too!

yours truly

Mr. Curly

x x x

Dear Mr. Curly,

I hope you are well. I'm still wandering far and wide, looking at the world, and now I realise and sort of accept that I am observing and am part of a world which is dying. This is certainly a sad understanding and seems to imply that life is not worth living but, strangely, this is not how I feel. The vital question now seems to be — shall our dear old earth die badly or well? This matters, I think, and seems to be worth working with and struggling with: how do we attend the dying earth? It seems peculiar to be grieving about a death which has not yet occurred and very confusing to mourn ahead of time but this seems a wise and proper thing to learn about because there will be no possibility of a requiem after the event; no fine words or music, and no tears — all those things which can help make sense of death and sweeten it. Perhaps, little by little, we can start doing this already; perhaps a cheerful vase of daffodils can also be, sometimes, a small wreath. We need to be careful with this however — and gentle too because what bothers me most is the feelings of the innocent children. Their hearts are not yet ready for such burdens. So how do we proceed with them? How do we _be_ with them? I must say that when I am amongst them I can only feel that all shall be well and I accept this happiness as a simple pleasure, but when they depart I grow troubled and sad.

How we have wallowed too deeply in the history of man's inhumanity to man — the endless stories of "who did what to whom" and how little we have known or cared or understood about man's cruel persecution of nature, the animals and the earth. Already the holocaust is well in motion and, as with the approaches of of all those other great tragedies and holocausts, — even when the writing is on the wall — we act as if the worst is not going to happen. In the light of all this, Curly, I ask you as I ask myself each morning, "WHAT is WORTH DOING AND WHAT IS WORTH HAVING?"

These are big questions and I am curious about your answers. I look forward to hearing from you. For the time being I have my faith and I am doing what I can.

Yours cheerfully

and entirely seriously

Vasco Pyjama

x xx

Dear Vasco,

in response to your question "What is worth doing and what is worth having?" I would like to say simply this. It is worth doing nothing and having a rest; in spite of all the difficulty it may cause, you must rest Vasco — otherwise you will become RESTLESS!

I believe the world is sick with exhaustion and dying of restlessness. While it is true that periods of weariness help the spirit to grow, the prolonged, ongoing state of fatigue to which our world seems to be rapidly adapting is ultimately soul destroying as well as earth destroying. The ecology of evil flourishes and love cannot take root in this sad situation. Tiredness is one of our strongest, most noble and instructive feelings. It is an important aspect of our CONSCIENCE and must be heeded or else we will not survive. When you are tired you must HAVE that feeling and you must act upon it sensibly — you MUST rest like the trees and animals do.

Yet tiredness has become a matter of shame! This is a dangerous development. Tiredness has become the most suppressed feeling in the world. Everywhere we see people overcoming their exhaustion and pushing on with intensity — cultivating the great mass mania which all around is making life so hard and ugly — so cruel and meaningless — so utterly graceless — and being congratulated for overcoming it and pushing it deep down inside themselves as if it were a

virtue to do this. And of course Vasco,
you know what happens when such
strong and natural feelings are denied —
they turn into the most powerful and
bitter poisons with dreadful consequences.
We live in a world of these consequences
and then wonder why we are so
unhappy.

So I gently urge you Vasco, do as
we do in Curly Flat — learn to curl up
and rest — feel your noble tiredness —
learn about it and make a generous
place for it in your life and enjoyment
will surely follow. I repeat: it's worth
doing nothing and having a rest.

yours sleepily,

Mr. Curly xxx

Dear Mr. Curly
the journey is livelier and more enjoyable
than ever. I attribute this to the fact
that I am losing my grasp of things. How
pleasing it is to lose ones grasp!

There is a time to grasp and a time
to hold and there has been too much
grasping and too little holding in this life.

Holding is of the arms and the breast
and the heart. It is steady in its nature and
requires commitment. Grasping rhymes with
gasping and is essential for certain
emergencies. It is a desperate activity of
the hands which would much rather be
touching, constructing, dismantling,
picking flowers, patting animals, scratching
the head or stroking the chin. I must
say however that in order to hold

something it is sometimes necessary
to grasp it first like a duck, after it
has been spooked by a sinister beast!
   Anyway Curly, I hold something very
dear to me which you said many years ago:
"The bird of paradise does not alight
on the hand that grasps."
   This is a helpful thing to understand
and I thank you for those words.
      And many others too!
         Yours faithfully,
              Vasco Pyjama

Dear Vasco,
swirling season has come to Curly Flat and there
is much much whirling and twirling.
    Wish you were here.
        Love, Mr. Curly.

Dear Mr. Curly. my heart is
heavy with a great sadness. It feels
like such an old, old sadness — so full
and still and beautiful; so painful.
I want to be with it. I want to
stay here and become like it.

with love.

Vasco Pyjama

P.S. IT FEELS SO, SORT OF, "WELL ROUNDED" TOO.

Dear Vasco,
here's a picture of me preparing to
water ski across Lake Lacuna.
I can only manage one ride a day
and that's in the evening when the
ducks fly home to roost on the
far side of the lake. I walk back
along the shore which looks quite

beautiful in the moonlight and I
often think of you then and wish
you well.

     Good health Vasco!
          Yours truly
             Mr. Curly.

P.S. That's a bread stick the ducks are
holding in their beaks!

Dear Mr. Curly,

I have done little travelling lately because I have been so dreadfully weary. Can it be true as old Ecclesiastes said; that all things lead to weariness? Surely not. Perhaps the opposite is true: that all nothings lead to weariness. I have a peculiar feeling Curly, that I am worn out from something I haven't yet done and the more I don't do it, the more exhausted I become. How strange. Could it be something I haven't said? Something I haven't realised? Perhaps it's something I haven't finished! It must be very large and true whatever it is and a lively struggle in the doing but I look forward to it immensely. I know I need it. First, however, I must curl up in my chair and sleep deeply with the duck.

Perhaps I'll dream of this thing and wake up refreshed and do it. My fond wishes to you Mr. Curly, and to all at Curly Flat.

Yours sleepily,

Vasco Pyjama
x x x

P.S. Not having breakfast can make you weary. THAT'S FOR SURE!

Dear Vasco,

how pleased I was to receive your letter. I trust that by now you have had sleep and rest enough to return to the enjoyment of your journey. What an achievement it is to sleep deeply; and what an achievement also to be wide awake. I suspect that one leads to the other. And be careful not to mix them together too much—keep them separate and distinct or you'll end up stuck in that troubled, tragic state of semi-consciousness into which so much of the world is always sliding: troubled sleep and trouble waking up: it cannot live well and it cannot die well, it just wears itself down. By the way Vasco, there's an old Curly Flat remedy for insomnia. In the garden you must dig a hole as deep as yourself and find a small stone in the bottom. Then climb out of the hole, fill it in and go inside to a good, delicious dinner and a glass or two of wine. Then go to bed with the stone under your pillow and lie there listening to it with your eyes closed. Soon you'll be asleep. Apparently it works!

Anyway, I'd better finish now; stay in touch — you'll always find me here.

Warm wishes Vasco and good luck!

yours sincerely Mr. Curly. xxx

P.S. Waking up: Now that's a big subject. Remedies there are many but how many of them actually work?!!!

Dear Mr. Curly,
I am still a little shaken having recently
witnessed, for the first time, something called
a "football match". It was awful. Two opposing
teams of men, with great skill and energy,
thwarted and violated each other, quite obsessively
and shamelessly in full view of a large crowd for
more than one and a half hours.

Such greed and desperate snatching I have
never seen before; such injury, sadism and
sabotage perpetrated in the cause of advantage
over one's fellows. I saw not the smallest
kindness or act of good faith pass between the
teams. More interestingly, the crowd was
utterly approving of all this trouncing and
hurting and deceiving — in fact it seemed
to thrive on it and became radiant when
the spectacle was most violent.

The questions that occur to me are: why do
people celebrate such primitive greed and
conflict — what _is_ this need? Why do
they desire an unbalanced outcome? What
do they mean when they say "It's just
a game" and why do they need to have
it out there in front of them but well and truly
removed from them — if they love it so much
why aren't they doing it themselves — thwarting
and grabbing and dominating and causing
pain and injury? — maybe they are, but in a

sneaky way, and they feel good to see it all
acted out in this big public ritual. Public
confession, I'd call it, and I guess that's not
a bad thing. Anyway the duck had a terrible
day but, as usual, took the spectacle of human
madness and sickness in its stride - or should
I say, "in its waddle". As we know, ducks
don't stride; nor are they strident!
Good wishes dear friend.

yours truly and in a waddling spirit
Vasco Pyjama.

43

Dear Vasco,
autumn has come once more to Curly Flat. The leaves
are falling, the days are becoming shorter and certain
birds have already departed. In the forest, yesterday
evening, I came upon a child crouched over a
tiny grave and placing flowers carefully around
the little cross made of twigs. I learned from
the child that it was a bird's grave and when
I asked what kind of bird the child, after a
long pause, simply replied, "a small, brown
bird." I left the child to its devotions and
passed on into a darker part of the forest,
with all its grandeur and peace, and was
there filled suddenly with a great grief
and also a great, tender joy and gladness
for what I had just seen. Then, a little
tearfully, I lay down on the forest floor
to contemplate the divinity of children
and small brown birds and, so doing,

I fell into a deep and blissful sleep on a bed of ferns. How I love the forest Vasco and how radiant is the autumn with all its dying and going to sleep.
Warm wishes to yourself and the duck
Yours truly,

Mr. Curly

P.S. Such tears and such sleeps are very good for the complexion, so I'm told!

Dear Mr. Curly,
what a pleasure it was to receive your
letter and hear of the beautiful autumn
in good old Curly Flat. I haven't got
any idea where I am at the moment and
don't mind not knowing for I most certainly
do not feel at all lost. You will be pleased
to know, I'm sure, that my direction-
finding duck is in excellent health —
feathers as white as an angel and beak
all gold and smooth like a good butternut
pumpkin. What a duck! The creature
seems so enthusiastic and occupied with
the business of just being a duck and
doesn't appear interested in anything more
or anything else. Come to think of it
Curly, in all of my travels I never once
met a duck which could be called a rich
duck or a famous duck — I never met a

religious duck or a fashionable duck or even a republican duck. Funny thing, that. They were always just ducks and quite dignified about it. I suspect they work pretty hard at that and good on them. And good on us as well Mr. Curly. You and me.

Yours sincerely,

Vasco Pyjama x x x

Dear Vasco,

it is the shortest day here in Curly Flat — the winter solstice. We had a very interesting time trying to measure this shortest day. How does one measure a day? Length is one matter but depth and width are just as important. For instance, a short day may be very deep or a long day may be shallow and narrow. What seems to be vital is whether or not the day is spacious, in which case the <u>roundedness</u> of the day is perhaps the most important factor. After all, a round day holds happiness most successfully — happiness itself being of a rounded shape, as you have observed.

The shortest day always reminds me that life is short but no sooner am I conscious of that than I am reminded that life is also very long. This is a most comforting paradox, for when I know that it is short, life seems more precious and sweet: I am overcome with a great sense of forgiveness and my sufferings seem more bearable and fleeting — in fact they almost feel like blessings. And when I know that life is long I am reassured and contented that the great wheel will surely turn and natural justice will come to pass most certainly. But once again Vasco, it is not the length of life which is important, it is the shape and the spaciousness—for therein lies the potential for a beautiful freedom. It is the roundness of life which matters. A round life is surely a happy life — and dare I say — it is a good life.

Please consider these reflections as a small picnic of thoughts we may share together — as we have shared picnics of sandwiches and wine on the shores of Lake Lacuna in summers past. Those were happy days — and they will come again.

    Fare well Vasco!

      with salutes and smiles,

        Mr. Curly.

Dear Mr. Curly,

I am writing to report a great and wonderful discovery. It is the discovery of my own stupidity and what a marvellous and enjoyable thing it is for me.

As my journey has become lonelier I have somehow grown more stupid in what I feel is a natural and comfortable way. Perhaps it is the fine example set by the duck or perhaps it is because there is nobody to chastise me with strictures or an intelligent gaze — the clever world can be so unforgiving, don't you think; so cruel and oppressive to the stupid part of our nature. Stupidity is like love, in this respect Curly, in that it will find a way and if it is suppressed or thwarted too much it will become a demon and enter surreptitiously into the world as cruelty, coldness or misery. The need to be clever and excellent and brilliant eventually brings a particular kind of weariness and the time comes to let dear old stupidity play its wonky hand. That time has come for me and I think the duck is relieved, as indeed I am.

So I feel, Curly, that I am leaving the vast continent

of solitude and entering the land of stupidity: my promised land and sanctuary of freedom: my lost country of new life and good sleep and forgiveness: my poor, long-suffering, beautiful stupidity — friend of my childhood, I have found you at last and I am coming home.

That's how it seems to me Mr. Curly and I find that I have quite a capacity for slow-wittedness and dumb silliness which seems to suit me down to the ground. I <u>like</u> it. There's almost a spiritual quality in it...! Come to think of it, the paintings I always liked the most were always a bit on the stupid side. Do you know what I mean Curly?

I'm sure you do.
Yours happily
Vasco Pyjama
x xx
P.S. I'm still quite clever too.

Dear Vasco,

I was delighted to receive your letter this morning and read the joyous news that you have finally embraced your stupidity and found such blessed relief. How very good for your heart Vasco. How marvellous! What a momentous achievement this embrace has been; and what a splendiferous liberation awaits you. What glorious songs the birds will now sing for you — great fugues of rapture, just you wait, as the miracle of your "beautiful stupidity" comes wobbling and clanking into your life and sets you free. My most extravagant congratulations Vasco and a warm welcome to the fold.

After I had read your letter I, straight away, seized my tin whistle and went up to the top field where I did a celebratory dance in your honour — a sort of weird jig. This was quite a stupid thing to do because the ground was slippery and muddy from the rain which was pelting down and I kept falling over and made quite a mess of my new corduroy trousers.

Still, I had a lovely bowl of soup for dinner this evening which was all the more delicious for me having fallen in the mud and I've never enjoyed a bowl of soup so much in all my life. It goes to show you, doesn't it. I'd better hop into bed now because I'm feeling very pleasantly sleepy.

The day is done.

Goodnight Vasco;

Yours truly,

Mr. Curly

x x x

Dear Vasco,

just a quick note from Curly Flat
to let you know the result of this
year's Ceremony of the Butterfly's Choice.
After much drama and nervous deliberation
on the part of the insect and much gasping
from the crowd, the butterfly finally
settled on the lavender. This, of course.

will be of consequence in the conduct of courtships, funerals, the teaching of songs to children and a host of other ordinary daily matters. The last time we had a lavender year many chickens came home to roost and I would welcome that were it to happen again. It was a very good year.

I must fly. Yours sincerely

Mr. Curly

Dear Mr. Curly,

no sooner do I graciously accept the huge, rollicking fact of my permanent stupidity and begin to laugh and enjoy it than I am quite suddenly overtaken by an astounding new vision of human madness. The wholeness and perfect clarity of the vision, its majestic, symphonic form is so profoundly moving — so utterly humbling and bracing that my heart, in response, has concocted from the elements of the revelation a strange calm energy - almost a rapture - which no doubt I will need in order to bear the consequences of such an insight.

Many times in the past I have deemed the world mad in a devil-may-care manner. How wise and satisfied I felt to say it like that. But now, and quite significantly I suspect, just as I have committed myself to the acceptance of my ongoing stupidity, I suddenly see the nature of madness as I have never seen it before and I am quite awestruck.

I'm not concerned here with the visible, pitiful madness of the grinning wretch who stands banging his head against a tree or the one who sits naked on a street corner rocking to and fro and weeping mournfully. Compassion can make some sense of this.

Instead I now behold the great, symphonic, invisible madness: the accumulating, collective, interactive madness called normal life: those millions of human lives, deeds and moments which in themselves seem in order but which, by the nature of their relationship, one to the other over time, amount to a massive miserable absurdity: the great undertow of human depravity, malice and wretchedness in which we must somehow conduct our lives. Perhaps I feel something of the awe and humility a lone sailor might feel as he sits in his very tiny boat, in the quiet of a brewing storm, and beholds all around and beneath him the great heaving ocean on which he must stay afloat and hold to his course.

I am a sailor on a sea of madness.

Ahoy there Mr. Curly!

yours faithfully,

Vasco Pyjama.

Dear Vasco,

the rose plants have just, this day, been made available at the Curly Flat rose farm. As usual, a small ensemble from the Academy of Ancient Music performed a selection of old airs and dances in celebration. I purchased two roses for my collection: "Baby's Bottom" and "Grandmother's Kiss". Like all roses from the farm the origins of these two plants are unknown; they are old "mystery roses" and, of course, the ensemble only played old music of unknown authorship, probably composed by birds in the dawn of history. "Baby's Bottom", as you might imagine, has a plump, rounded flower with pink petals of the most delicate texture and colour. The perfume is delightfully reminiscent of a baby's breath.

"Grandmother's kiss" has a large, blowsy, crinkled
flower with an abundance of big loose petals
of deep crimson. It has a distinct "handbag"
fragrance which comes in great volumes and
alters markedly as the day progresses. The
evening aroma is quite different to the aroma
of the morning.

How arresting is the credential, "unknown
origin"! How deep and rich it seems. How

vibrant and free and magical, like a talisman, seems that creature, that plant or that thing of "unknown origin".

Enjoy the sea of madness Vasco. It is the wildest of the seven seas certainly, but the most wondrous sailing can be had there. Above you is the sky of gladness, all so full of ancient music and babies' breath and birds and the perfume of roses!

Good health Vasco
yours faithfully

Mr. Curly.

Dear Vasco,

although spring seems to be arriving cautiously this year in Curly Flat, the doves have started mating with remarkable vigour and conviction. The courtship dances of doves are studied with serious interest in Curly Flat. With careful interpretation these little tangos and flamencos reveal much about the current state of nature and prospects for the coming season. Judging by recent performances I would say that we're in for a summer of "considerable character". I don't recall when I last saw so much ardour combined with such dash and flamboyance. There is an unusually strong sense of glee and purpose in the doves this year and as well as being inspiring and delightful to watch, I think it bodes well generally.

Birds are such good teachers, Vasco, in many things, but particularly in the matters of making music and making love. If we could do these things with as much conviction as they do we would surely fly like them as a simple consequence.

I'll write again soon, but for the moment there's something I want to do in the garden. I must fly. All good wishes dear friend.

Yours truly

Mr. Curly xxx

65

Dear Vasco,

spring has come once more to Curly Flat
and the roses are starting to bloom. How
contented I feel as I contemplate the roses.
How complete life seems in the presence of
these ancient perfumes and petals. How
liberated from the desire to "better" myself
and how sweetly intoxicated I am by these
dear, precious moments of self-acceptance
given to me, so generously, by the rose. Around
me, in the morning sunshine, the bees hum and
various unseen fowls warble old songs concerning
the arrival of good blue eggs. Along the
shores of Lake Lacuna, over the water and
from the small valleys around Curly Flat
I hear the occasional pealing of the life-
goes-on bells — simple declarations from

the distance that life is worth living —
a domestic prayer from an unknown household,
rung out in thanksgiving for the morning
now passing and announcing that the
afternoon and its pleasures and duties are
soon to begin ____ or perhaps a chimed
observance that sadness has passed in a
particular home and that relief and
gratitude have begun ____ any of life's
ordinary precious moments being honoured
as they come and go by whoever is taken by
the impulse to do so. How brave and reassuring
are the bells of Curly Flat — bells of
spontaneity; bells of acceptance; bells of joy
and simple duty: life-goes-on bells! Perhaps

you still hear them Vasco, ringing in your
dreams; I hope so.

The sound of a bell and the perfume of a rose: these things cannot be improved — they are perfectly complete. Warmest spring wishes.

Go well vasco
and ding dong!
with love,
Mr. Curly

Dear Vasco,
I've composed a little poem for
you in honour of spring; it's a
tongue twister called "Friends
Like Fronds".

I'm fond of friends like fronds.
I am Quite frondly, I would say.
Friends behave like fronds and fronds
Like friends in every way.

    I hope you like it.
      yours frondly
        Mr. Curly.

Dear Mr. Curly,

Greetings! I hope this message reaches you before December 25th because I want to wish you and the others at Curly Flat a most merry and curly christmas — and a nicely resolved one too. A bit of clarity makes a very lovely Christmas decoration I say!

I won't be home for the big day and feel not a scrap of homesickness about that. Christmas used to disturb me a bit — you know, all that yearning — but not so much any more. I now think that homesickness comes from sick homes — unresolved homes! Anyway Curly, I'm beginning to think that my true home is in heaven and I don't want to go there on christmas day. On the subject of sickness and greetings, I saw a mysterious old inscription above a doorway on my travels recently. I pass it on to you for your contemplation: "better the kiss of a leper than the handshake of

a fool." I have pondered much on that
and feel it to be important. What do
you think?

In closing I will say that, more than ever,
I share your love of the christmas music
and will be with you in spirit as I sing those
carols with the duck beneath beautiful stars
on christmas eve. Peace be with you Mr. Curly.

Yours truly,

Vasco Pyjama
x x x

P.S. "The handshake of a foolish leper" - that's a
worrying thought!

P.P.S "Clarity begins at home" - that's a
good thought!

Dear Vasco Pyjama

It is autumn in Curly Flat. Something vast and marvellous is coming to an end. How perfect and radiant is the death of anything which has run its true course. How beautiful is the death of summer, dear Vasco. Perhaps only that which is true can complete itself.

How this poor world is crowded and poisoned and choked with unfinished business. We must make way for new life! As I write, I hear children in the distance singing sad little eulogies for the fallen leaves. It is late in the afternoon but the sun is shining very brightly. Perhaps this is the best place to finish my letter. Be careful Vasco. Much love — yours sincerely

Mr. Curly

Dear Mr Curly,

it's springtime
where I am at present; the
sun is shining and the birds
are singing beautifully —
life is a miracle. There are
so many astonishing and
wonderful things to talk about.
I'll write again soon.

lots of warm wishes,

Vasco.

P.S. A great thing has happened.
I've fallen in love.